CONTENTS

Page

front page at back!

suffered hardship or injustice as a result of failure of service or failure to provide a service or maladministration.

13. <u>Prescribing and Dispensing</u>. The emphasis of the pilots is on new approaches to general medical services. It is not intended to change the basic arrangements for dispensing (by community pharmacists or "dispensing" doctors) or prescribing (by doctors or nurses). Pilots would be able to opt for the flexibility to move funding between prescribing and other budgets, following the example of fundholding, otherwise the same arrangements would apply as for non-fundholders.

14. <u>Accounts and Audit</u>. Because pilots might involve different ways of meeting pay and expenses, contracts may need to specify how accounts relating to the pilot should be kept and for there to be access to the relevant part. And, as with fundholding, the Comptroller and Auditor General should be able to inspect these accounts.

15. <u>Dental Charges</u>. A national scale of dental charges will apply for all charge paying adults receiving treatment under the GDS, or pilots of the new system. The current exemptions and remissions will remain in place, as will the maximum charge per course of treatment. Charges will be collected by the practitioner and netted off payments by the health authority or board.

16 <u>Prior Approval</u>. For more expensive and the most complex dental treatments a system of prior approval will be maintained. This will be to the specifications of the purchasing health authority or board.

17. <u>National Safeguards</u>. Although there will be considerable flexibility for local people to determine the arrangements which best suit them, the legislation should ensure that there are national safeguards for patients, taxpayers and practitioners (as there are under the current arrangements). In particular, the Secretary of State should be able to:

- require health authorities or boards to consult locally on the proposed pilot;

- decide which pilots will go ahead. Only those which he approves will be able to do so;

- decide elements which must appear in any contracts and the way in which they must do so;

- ensure that practitioners can return to the Medical List if pilots end, subject to the points set out above;

- end a pilot if that seemed appropriate in the interests of the NHS;

- ringfence money transferred to health authorities or boards for the piloting of new methods of delivering GMS and GDS;

p-19.

FOREWORD

The development of primary care is fundamental to maintaining and strengthening the National Health Service. The wide ranging consultations on primary care services have revealed a strong sense of how the service might be developed, the opportunities which could be encouraged and the improvements which could result. They have also clearly demonstrated the commitment of health professionals and managers to good quality primary care and how patients could benefit. Offering greater choice and opportunity to those working within primary care so that services can more closely meet the needs of local people and so that managers and professionals can more easily provide them, has been one of the major themes to emerge. We wish to respond to those desires and positively to follow up points made during consultation with action. We do not consider this the sole response necessary but it is right that it should be done in advance of the remainder because of its implications for legislation. It inevitably concentrates on those most directly affected, GPs, dentists, pharmacists and optometrists but it also recognises the implications for nurses, health visitors, midwives, therapists, and managers and others who work in primary care and are so important to its successful delivery. Our aim is to enable local people to develop services which will more closely fit their and the local service needs. We have no template in mind. The essence of the proposals for primary care contained in this document are choice, opportunity and flexibility for those providing services, while ensuring high standards for patients, consistent quality across the country and good value for money within the resources available.

STEPHEN DORRELL

MICHAEL FORSYTH   WILLIAM HAGUE

Chapter 1

INTRODUCTION

1.1 Over the last year, there has been a wide debate about the future development of primary care. It has engaged professionals, patients and managers. Participants have identified the opportunities as well as the barriers to developments. A set of principles against which existing services could be measured and future development determined has been established. An agenda, identifying the kind of actions which are necessary to enable primary care services to develop to their potential to meet patient's needs and for primary care professionals to have rewarding and satisfying careers, has begun to emerge.

1.2 These debates have been summarised in England in "Primary Care: The Future" (subsequently confirmed in the Minister for Health's "agenda setting round") and in Wales in "Primary Care : The Way Forward in Wales". In Scotland, there has been extensive discussion with the service based on the draft paper "Primary Care – The Way Ahead", this has built on the earlier "Framework for Action in Primary Care".

1.3 All the discussion and the documents have pointed to an agenda for action which embraces all aspects of primary care and the professionals working within it as well as managers and patients. It is now essential to begin to take the agenda forward if we are to develop primary care services in the way that patients, health professionals and managers want. The Government intends to bring forward broader proposals later in the autumn to address the issues identified from the discussions in England, Wales and Scotland.

1.4 However, a clear message from all the consultations has been the need for action to encourage "local flexibility so that services can be delivered in a way which is better attuned to local needs and circumstances". More flexible arrangements for providing family health services were seen as essential to the following objectives:

- **to promote consistently high quality services across the country. The organisation of these services, the mix of primary care professionals and the use of financial resources should be sufficiently flexible to meet local needs effectively;**

- **to provide opportunities and incentives for primary care professionals to use their skills to the full. The current legislative and contractual framework prevents this happening;**

- **to provide more flexible employment opportunities in primary care. The primary care workforce is changing, particularly in general practice, and employment arrangements have not always kept pace with the changing needs and aspirations of GPs and other health professionals and managers who work in primary care.**

1.5 Proposals have been made for new contractual opportunities which could support these objectives in some places. But a consistent message throughout the debate on primary care has been that changes of that sort should be by consent and consultation involving volunteers; and that they should be taken forward through pilots with proper evaluation.

1.6 These themes have many similarities with those which emerged from the longer period of discussion and debate on primary care dentistry. Over the last few years this, too, has involved extensive consultation with the representative bodies of the dental profession and individual dentists, as well as with NHS managers and patients' representatives. In the short term, this led to the Government's proposals for reform of general dental practitioners' remuneration which were agreed with the profession in May 1996 and took effect from 1 September. Alongside this there emerged the view that, over the longer term, there should be a move towards greater local sensitivity in the provision of dental services. This was set out as a Government objective in the 1994 Green Paper "Improving NHS Dentistry".

1.7 To allow greater local flexibility, there will need to be changes in legislation as the current arrangements, some of which date from the start of the NHS nearly 50 years ago, are too rigid to allow the flexibility now sought. The Government accepts that having listened to views and consulted on the need for greater flexibility it should now act. It therefore intends to bring forward such legislation. This document sets out the proposed shape of the legislation. In doing so, it inevitably concentrates on those professions which will be most directly involved – general medical and dental practitioners, community pharmacists and optometrists.

1.8 It also recognises that changes are required to help develop the contribution which nurses, midwives and health visitors and the professions allied to medicine can make. They have an equally important part to play in providing primary care and the changes proposed have implications for them both in their wider involvement in any pilots which are subsequently introduced following legislation but also in the opportunities which different approaches may offer to develop further the team based approach which is essential to good quality primary care.

1.9 This document also addresses a further issue for which legislation is needed. The system of appointing GPs to single handed practices has long been criticised. The Government proposes to bring forward legislation in line with the recommendations in "Maintaining Medical Excellence", a report by the Chief Medical Officer. This proposed that the relevant primary legislation be reviewed at the earliest opportunity to ensure that appointments to practice vacancies were only made when at least one of the candidates met the standards set out in the job description. This recommendation has been widely supported throughout the medical profession and by NHS managers. At the same time, the Government believes it would be right to reduce some of the bureaucracy surrounding GP appointments. In keeping with generally accepted principles, practice appointments need to secure the right manpower and skill mix to meet local needs. The process also needs to allow professionals and managers to get on with the job without being encumbered by unnecessary rules and regulations.

Chapter 2.

GENERAL PRACTICE

Wider Contractual Choice

2.1   Primary care, and general practice in particular, has developed a great deal over the last decade.   Care once confined to specialist hospitals can now be provided much closer to patients' homes. GP fundholding and the wider drive to involve GPs in commissioning health services have shown both how primary care can develop and also demonstrated the strong and beneficial influence it can have on hospital services. These trends will continue. There are great opportunities to develop a wider range of services in primary care given continued advances in technology and professional practice. But this will also require the development of the infrastructure necessary to support it, and the allocation of an appropriate share of the resources available to the NHS to underpin it.

2.2   GPs, and the Primary Health Care Team, have already shown that they can considerably improve the range and quality of services available as well as the efficiency with which they are delivered, given the right opportunities, incentives and resources. But these opportunities have also brought pressures and stresses. Changes to the workforce have also added new demands, and some long standing problems have not been addressed fully.

2.3   The debate on primary care has clearly identified a number of issues which need to be tackled for general practice to continue to develop and primary care services to improve:

-    although generally good, the quality of service for some patient groups and in some areas is not always high. New ways need to be found to address these problems, some of which are long standing;

-    the rewards and incentives of the single national contract do not always have a clear link to the services required to meet local needs or circumstances;

-    similarly, the contract does not always promote the team approach often needed in primary care or the opportunities available for GPs to combine with other professions, for example nurses or therapists, to their mutual benefit to deliver services to patients;

-    fundholding and the move towards a Primary Care led NHS has placed wider responsibilities on GPs as well as offering wider opportunities. The distinction between what constitutes general medical services, (that is, the GPs' traditional role) and provision of other services in a general practice setting is becoming increasingly blurred;

- the traditional structure of general practice based on partnerships, personal investment and long term commitments does not always meet the different needs or aspirations of existing, or possible future, GPs. Career breaks, part time working and changes in career or location are becoming increasingly common features and, alongside problems of GP recruitment in some areas, are challenging traditional models.

2.4 In many cases, the existing basic arrangements substantially meet both the service needs and the needs of the general practitioner. They are already delivering good quality care and can see their way to develop further within the existing framework. In these circumstances little, if any, change is required other than perhaps a little fine tuning. In other circumstances, this is not the case. The pressures or the service needs may be substantially different or local people can see opportunities for development which are currently barred but which will bring benefits to patients and provide more satisfying careers. In those cases, more radical action may be needed. During the debate on the future of primary care, a number of ideas were suggested which it was thought could offer ways forward and open new possibilities and opportunities for addressing service issues. These included:

- **a salaried option for GPs, either within partnerships or with other bodies, such as NHS trusts.** This may offer ways to improve some inner city services and to free doctors from business as opposed to clinical responsibilities. It may be attractive to some, providing a wider range of employment opportunities to fit in with individuals' lifestyles while also allowing more scope to tailor all the primary health care services provided to the needs of an area;

- **practice based contracts.** These could more easily reflect the nature of practice in many areas and embrace non-medical professionals, including nurses, therapists and managers, opening new possibilities for development of skill mix and careers;

- **a single budget for general medical services, other hospital and community health services, and prescribing with the practice responsible for purchasing or providing services within it.** Some, particularly some fundholders, considered that such a mixture of fundholding and a practice based contract would help secure more integrated, more efficient and better services for patients.

2.5 All these ideas could bring benefits both to patients and professionals but the current legislative framework, dating substantially from 1948, effectively prevents them because:

- contracts must be made with individual GPs, not practices. There are also some positive disincentives for practices who want to replace a doctor with a nurse even where this might be more efficient and provide better patient services;

- only the Secretary of State can set the terms of the contract, ruling out local flexibility;

- a salaried option, other than as an assistant or associate, is effectively ruled out;

- there is a strict division between the funding and arrangements made for general medical services on the one hand and hospital and community health services on the other.

2.6 While there is considerable interest in trying out these ideas, there was no enthusiasm for moving directly to any or all of these options without careful exploration first and no enthusiasm for forced change : the existing contractual arrangements should therefore continue alongside any new approaches.

2.7 The Government shares this view and intends to bring forward legislation to enable wider contractual choices to be tested and made available. The legislation will enable those who wish to do so to pilot different types of contract to test their practical implications and the benefits they could bring. If these pilots are successful it should then be possible to generalise any arrangements from the experience gained, so as to develop a range of approaches which have been first tested in practice. The overriding aim must be to deliver to patients high quality primary care and within that high quality general medical services from well motivated professionals.

2.8 The debates over the last year have made clear that, interest in exploring new contractual arrangements must also be tempered by concerns about what the effect of these might be and whether valuable elements of primary care might be lost in any transition. Accordingly the Government believes that a number of key principles should apply to the legislation.

1. Participation in new approaches to general practice contracts should be voluntary. No doctor should be required to take part in them or to change their existing arrangements.

2. Patients must continue to have a right to be registered with a GP, and to be able to choose their GP. This should secure the essential character of British general practice which provides personal lists, continuity of care and personal service based on a relationship between an individual and his or her GP and the responsibility that the doctor carries.

3. The legislation should allow different types of arrangements to be piloted and for pilots to be evaluated before being opened more widely.

4. The legislation should enable local flexibility but also ensure that there are adequate national safeguards for both patients and practitioners.

5. Pilots and new arrangements should emerge from the field and be subject to discussion locally amongst those affected, including other health care

2.9 Piloting the new arrangements will not be appropriate for many practices. However, the Government recognises that a number of GPs who wish to retain the existing contract may nonetheless identify ways in which general medical services could be further developed locally to the benefit of patients given the right incentives. Possibilities here, for example, would be locally developed chronic disease management programme which went beyond asthma and diabetes, or services to a particular group of patients, say, the mentally ill, which needed development. These arrangements are not possible now as general medical services are the sole province of the national contract.

2.10 The Government therefore proposes to make provision to enable health authorities or boards to reach agreement with GPs locally to develop specific areas of general medical services. Health authorities and boards would be able to make extra payments locally for GMS over and above the national fees and allowances. Such payments would be funded from health authorities' general cash limited resources for hospital and community health services, and would not count against GPs intended average income.

2.11 Details of how the legislation would enable pilots to operate the flexibilities which it would offer and the national safeguards which it would provide are set out in Appendix A. This document deals only with the main aspects of the legislation which will provide a framework for piloting and introducing new ideas which will offer GPs greater choice and opportunity to develop services alongside health authorities. A great deal of detailed work will be necessary to develop the arrangements and to work up the details of pilots. The Government is looking to work constructively and closely with primary care team members and health service managers to develop these ideas and particularly with GPs and their representatives, both nationally and locally.

GP APPOINTMENTS

2.12 Under the current legislation, health authorities and boards are responsible for appointing GPs to vacancies in single handed practices. They are required to appoint from the list of candidates once the post has been advertised a maximum of three times, regardless of the suitability of the individuals available for that particular practice. This arrangement has been strongly criticised, most recently in the report "Maintaining Medical Excellence" which has been widely endorsed. That report recommended that primary legislation should be reviewed at the earliest opportunity to ensure that appointments to vacancies were only made when at least one candidate met the standards set out in the job description. Although this could mean that a vacancy would remain when no candidate satisfied the criteria for appointment, this was considered important for maintaining quality.

2.13 The Government shares this view. <u>It intends to bring forward legislation to ensure that health authorities are not forced to appoint a GP to a single handed practice unless they are satisfied about the individual's suitability for the post</u>. Similar considerations apply in Scotland.

2.14 At the same time, the Government considers that two other issues need to be addressed. First, the existing legislation makes no distinctions between the arrangements for appointing a GP to a single handed practice or to a group practice. Therefore, it is the health authority's or board's responsibility to advertise and appoint practitioners to vacancies in group practices. This is clearly illogical as the prime responsibility for recruiting to a vacancy in a group practice and ensuring that he or she can provide the service required should rest with the other partners, although the health authority or board still needs to discharge its responsibility for the overall provision of services to its residents and the workforce required to provide them. The Government therefore intends to ensure that the law should properly reflect the fact that partners rather than health authorities or boards should select candidates for vacancies in group practices and that the onus is on them to confirm to the health authority or board that the new doctor can meet the service needs.

2.15 Second, under the current arrangements, the Medical Practices Committee has an important role in deciding upon the distribution of doctors throughout England and Wales. It does so by deciding whether there is a vacancy for a doctor, that is whether there are enough doctors in an area to meet the needs of the population compared with elsewhere. Once a vacancy has been declared and recruitment undertaken locally the MPC then admits the doctor to the Medical List for that health authority. This is automatic, the only test being whether a doctor is properly qualified. There is obvious scope for increased bureaucracy here as each appointment has to be considered twice, although the second occasion is a formality. The Government believes that formal admission to the list should be managed locally although the role of the MPC under the current arrangements in deciding on the distribution of GPs should be retained. Under the proposed legislation health authorities would formally admit GPs to the Medical List as a consequence of either their own proper recruitment exercise or following the selection of an appropriate candidate by an existing practice. A similar approach should also apply to the role of the Scottish Medical Practices Committee in Scotland.

Chapter 3.

COMMUNITY PHARMACY AND OPTOMETRY

3.1   Community Pharmacy services cover the dispensing of drugs, medicines and certain listed appliances for patients in a health authority area or board area. Other services can be prescribed by Parliament and currently include providing advice to residential and nursing homes and maintaining patient medication records. All these services are provided under Part II of the NHS Act 1977 or the NHS (Scotland) Act 1978.

3.2   The debate on primary care acknowledged the important role of community pharmacists in providing a wide range of services. It also recognised the wide support there was for new services that were being delivered better to meet patient needs and which were bringing pharmacists more closely within the primary health care team.

3.3   Several themes have emerged for taking forward the further development of community pharmacy. These are:

-    facilitating better use of prescribed medicines;

-    wider recognition of community pharmacy as the first port of call for minor ailments;

-    health promotion; and

-    providing more advice on medicines to the rest of the primary health care team and others.

3.4   Barriers to these developments were also identified. One of the most significant was the way that the current legislation constrained the range and standards of community pharmacy services and prevented these from being tailored to local needs. For example, community pharmacists are obliged to meet the national standards laid out – no more and no less. There is no legal basis for requiring them to provide a different level of service. Regulations can therefore act as a ceiling to service developments. Also, any community pharmacy which meets the requirements of the regulations can provide any prescribed service. This can cut across local needs and priorities, for example, where the service is needed in one neighbourhood rather than another. This can make financial planning difficult and, at worst, may not be cost effective.

3.5   Health authorities and boards also have no power to make arrangements for community pharmacy services with a pharmacy outside their boundaries. This prevents pharmacies from providing any services, such as domiciliary visits, to patients who live within another health authority or board's borders. This can cause inconvenience and inhibit effective patient care by forcing patients to choose an unfamiliar pharmacy which may be further away.

legalisation which will:

- allow health authorities and boards *flexibility*, to decide which, where and how much of the prescribed community pharmacy service to purchase while sticking to a basic framework and only purchasing from NHS community pharmacy;

- allow NHS community pharmacies to apply to provide these services from a local or neighbouring health authority or board.

3.8 Patients' long-standing right to take their NHS prescriptions to the community pharmacy of their choice will remain fully protected. <u>These proposals do not affect the community pharmacy dispensing service and the legal controls and standards which surround it</u>.

3.9 Under the intended legislation, the Secretary of State would set out in directions the pharmaceutical services which could be purchased locally by health authorities and boards. These might include services for individual patients, such as helping patients continue with their regime of treatment by, for example, giving extra counselling; or they may be directed at groups of patients or carers by raising awareness of medicine-related issues with them and helping with specific problems. They would also set criteria to ensure that services would only be performed by those who were competent to do so.

3.10 These local services may also involve acting as a back-up resource, providing help and advice on medicines to other health care staff. This would be within a framework for decisions which could include national minimum service standards for the general service. For example, a pharmacist providing medication review services for patients on a large number of medicines might be required to assess patients' medication in line with nationally specified criteria and liaise with the patients' GP. However, the health authority or board could decide whether they wished to set their own objectives or guidelines for medication review programmes and also prioritise services for particular patient groups.

3.11 A health authority or board would consider how much of these services it wished to purchase, what aspects or local specifications needed to be included, and how much they proposed to pay. There might be different entry criteria and variants of service for different patient types and in different localities within a single health authority or board. Following consultation they would determine these arrangements. NHS community pharmacies could then apply to provide the services. The health authority or board would be able to choose which applications to accept.

3.12 The Secretary of State would also be able to set out the criteria which health authorities and boards should use in making their decisions, although the emphasis would be on meeting local priorities and needs. Health authorities and boards would also be expected to consult about any particular service, including the broad form it should take and to whom it should be available. The Government would also expect health authorities and boards to consult locally on the details of the form and level of payment and on the way services would be delivered.

3.13 Health authorities and boards also have wide ranging powers under Part I of the NHS Act 1977 (NHS (Scotland) Act 1978) to purchase health services. These can be provided by anyone who can show that they are competent to do so. In recent years several services generally, but not exclusively, associated with community pharmacy, such as needle and syringe exchange schemes, have been purchased in this way. Some shared care schemes for optometry are also established under these powers.

3.14 Where health authorities or boards are already purchasing services in this way, they are obliged to do this using legally enforceable contracts. This has sometimes discouraged them from approaching NHS community pharmacists, or even considering them as potential providers for a wider range of services. The Government believes there would be benefits if these arrangements could be made through NHS contracts. They are usually simpler than ordinary contracts and are not enforceable by law, although they are subject to binding arbitration by the Secretary of State.

3.15 Many of the proposals raised in the debate on primary care for optometry services could be implemented within current legislation and consultation is already underway about the development of these services. However, there would be similar benefits if contracts between health authorities or boards and optometrists could be made NHS contracts and provision for this will also be made in the proposed legislation.

3.16 This, and the other proposals for legislation, would reinforce community pharmacy and optometry's place among NHS professionals in primary care.

Chapter 4.

DENTISTRY

New Means of Providing Services

4.1 The proposal to move to a "locally sensitive" system for providing primary care dentistry was initially set out in Sir Kenneth Bloomfield's fundamental review of the GDP remuneration system and was also put forward in the Health Select Committee's 1993 report on dental services. The Government's 1994 Green Paper "Improving NHS Dentistry" developed the proposal further. It suggested that a system might be set up, drawing on that already in place in the hospital and community health services, under which health authorities or boards would assess the demand and need for dental services in their areas and would be given budgets from which to purchase appropriate services from local dentists and other providers.

4.2 Such a system should make the delivery of services and their funding more responsive to local needs, producing better services for patients and better value for money. It could also provide scope for dentists who were frustrated by the constraints of a rigid central system to work together with local NHS managers to develop services which made the most of professional dental experience and commitment.

4.3 At the same time, the Government recognised that this approach could not simply mirror arrangements in the secondary care sector but would need to be developed to take account of the independent contractor status of dentists and the unique way in which they worked. It therefore made a commitment to carry out careful piloting and evaluation before considering wider implementation.

4.4 The Green Paper proposals were the subject of wide-ranging consultation with the profession and others with an interest. This was followed by further discussions, including a major one-day conference in October 1995, addressed by representatives of the profession, the NHS and the NHS Executive. These confirmed support for the proposal to pilot alternative arrangements. It also helped crystallise a number of other key themes, all related to the need to improve services to patients and the efficiency with which they are delivered:

- the need to balance the flexibility necessary to address local needs with the requirement for a standard national framework, for example in relation to patient charges or complaints arrangements;

- the need for change to be gradual and evolutionary in order to maintain a stable environment in which dentists are able to invest in their practices without undue risk; this might mean alternative approaches initially following current service patterns;

- the need for health authorities or boards and dentists to work together on the basis of mutual understanding, with dentists closely involved in service planning and the development of new approaches;

- the need for improved information on demography, disease experience, casemix and treatment volumes to underpin decisions on local service provision; infirmation technology may have a crucial role to play as would, again, cooperation between health authorities or boards and dentists.

4.5 The Government intends to be guided by these themes in taking forward its policy. As a first step, the necessary legislation needs to be put in place. As with the general medical services, the current legislative framework dates from 1948 and effectively stops alternative arrangements from being implemented.

4.6 It is not the intention that the legislation should prescribe in detail the form that alternative approaches should take. Because different approaches to service delivery may be appropriate to different areas and different circumstances, we need to ensure that a range of models can be tested during the pilot phase. Although we anticipate that in most cases primary care dentistry will continue to be provided by general dental practitioners, these models might also include contracts with practices or groups of practices, rather than individuals, or with NHS trusts employing dentists who wish to be free of the business responsibilities involved in running a practice. Contracts might vary from those involving only small modification to the existing national system to a system of sessional fees or the provision of a full range of services for a certain catchment population.

4.7 In order to allow for this diversity of possible models, the Government intends that the legislation should set out a broad framework within which contracting can develop through pilots. But these should also be underpinned by certain key features which should apply in all cases:

- participation should be voluntary. No dentist should be required to take part in it or to change their existing arrangements;

- dentists should be able to contract with health authorities or boards for some of their patients under the new arrangements while continuing to treat other patients under the current system;

- patients should continue to have a right to choose the dental practitioner from whom to receive dental treatment, subject to the consent of the practitioner.

4.8 The Government's proposals for legislation, to enable piloting to go ahead in general medical as well as dental services, are set out in Appendix A. Subject to Parliament's approval of the legislation, pilots would be established and evaluated. If evaluation demonstrates that these are successful, it will then be possible to generalise the arrangements from the experience gained, so as to develop a range of approaches which have been first tested in practice. The legislation will allow for this.

4.9   Much detailed work will be needed to develop the detailed arrangements for piloting, invite applications for pilot sites and then to ensure that these are ready to operate from the date of implementation. The Government attaches great importance to the continued input of the dental profession to this preparatory process and welcomes the commitment of the General Dental Services Committee of the BDA to work constructively with it on the piloting of contracting.

Appendix A

DETAILS OF PROPOSED LEGISLATION FOR PILOTING DIFFERENT APPROACHES FOR GENERAL MEDICAL AND GENERAL DENTAL SERVICES

1. The Government considers that there are strong similarities in the ideas being put forward for piloting different approaches to contracting for general medical and general dental services. It therefore believes that the broad approach should be similar whilst recognising that there will be difference in detail.

2. <u>Piloting</u>. The Government considers that the following general approach should apply to the pilots

- ideas for alternative forms of contracting for general medical or dental services should be formulated locally and could come initially from, for example, GPs, dentists, NHS trusts, health authorities or health boards. As they are developed, there would need to be a partnership between those involved;

- each proposal should consider not only the future contractual arrangement but the service problems it is intended to address through the new arrangement and the benefits it will bring;

- an outline would then be submitted to the Secretary of State. If it seemed worth pursuing the proposal should be worked up in detail, including more detailed local consultation of those affected, i.e. other health professionals and organisations, before being put forward by the health authority or board with their comments to the relevant Secretary of State for approval;

- as part of that approval, the Secretary of State would need to consider the form and nature of the arrangement proposed, whether it was likely to meet the objectives set for it including offering value for money and agree criteria on how the pilot should be evaluated;

- once approved, the pilot would run for the specified period of time, unless problems arose in which case fresh approval would be needed for changes to the pilot or, in the most serious cases, approval might be withdrawn and the pilot terminated;

- pilots would need careful project management and support throughout this time. There would be an important role for health authorities and boards and in England, NHS Executive Regional Offices in helping to develop and support pilots;

- funds would need to be transferred nationally and locally to support the new arrangement, leaving practitioners retaining the existing contractual arrangements neither better nor worse off. It will be important not to create inequity of resources for patients of different practices;

- details of the pilot would need to be made available both nationally and locally;

- pilots should be evaluated against the criteria established at the start and taking account of the views of those involved and affected.

3. Once a number of pilots had been evaluated and shown to be successful, central approval for similar arrangements might no longer be required. Such a move would need to be debated and discussed nationally and the necessary regulations to put this into effect subject to Parliamentary scrutiny before being introduced.

4. The type of pilots which might come forward are potentially wide in scope. Considerable flexibility will therefore have to be built in to any arrangements. The Government considers that this could most readily be achieved by enabling health authorities or boards to agree contracts for general medical and dental services in the circumstances set out above in the same way as they do for hospital and community health services now. This would provide the necessary scope and flexibility given the wide powers and the wide range of contracts that are already available there. This could be done by bringing general medical and dental services into Part I of the 1977 NHS Act (NHS (Scotland) Act 1978 in Scotland) for those that wished to take part in pilots or any longer term arrangements which might flow from them. The existing arrangements under Part II of the 1977 NHS Act and the NHS (Scotland) Act 1978 will remain available for those that wished to work as a GP or dentist under the current contract.

5. Patients' Interests. It will be important to ensure that patients' rights, currently secured in the existing arrangements, are also covered in the alternative approaches. Specifically, the Government intends that a patient's right to be registered with a GP of their choice should be retained. Equally, a doctor's right to refuse to add a patient to his or her list would also need to be retained together with the obligation commensurate with all other GPs in the area to accept patients allocated to them by health authorities or boards if that proved necessary in individual cases. Similarly, any new arrangements could not override the national and European requirements relating to qualification as a GP and the services they can provide. Patients would also continue to have a right to choose the dental practitioner who treated them, subject to the dentist's consent.

6. Detailed Arrangements for Pilots. Subject to these overriding considerations there will be much scope for the details of the services to be provided and the contract which will underpin them, including remuneration arrangements, to be worked out at local level in a way which properly reflects local needs and circumstances and the views of those involved. They would be tested against a national framework, including the general standards which should apply to all primary care services and which, for example, are set out in "Primary Care: The Future".

7. Contracts could reflect the full range of services which a practice might provide or could be more limited in scope, for example effectively confined to existing general medical or dental services. In general practice they could also allow practices to purchase or provide health care for their patients. This would offer greater flexibility than the existing fundholding arrangements, not only through the inclusion of general medical services but also by the ability to change the scope of the practice's responsibilities for purchasing or providing services by local agreement. Decisions about the way in which services could be provided or purchased under such contracts and any changes brought about as a result would of course need to be guided by the rules and guidance which relate to all such decisions, including for example prior discussion with the NHS trusts and staff likely to be affected. Although the overall arrangement could offer many advantages, the Government is conscious that some fundholding GPs might wish to pilot new GMS contracts but also to keep the fixed national arrangements which apply to fundholding – i.e. to keep their fundholding status. This option would therefore be made available.

8. Contracts could either be NHS or ordinary contracts. There are advantages and disadvantages to both. Health authorities, health boards and other Health Service bodies including NHS trusts and fundholders purchase services with each other using NHS contracts. They are usually simpler than ordinary contracts and are not enforceable by law, although they are subject to binding arbitration by the Secretary of State. Ordinary contracts would be used when services were provided outside the NHS. The Government considers that NHS contracts would normally be used for pilots and, if successful, over the longer term, particularly where for example, a practice would also be purchasing services from other Health Service bodies as with fundholding.

9. However, it seems sensible to leave the position open between NHS and ordinary contracts particularly in the early days of pilots so that those involved have a choice and the relative merits of the approaches can be assessed. As a failsafe, any arbitration made by the Secretary of State relating to payment could, if necessary, be pursued through the civil courts.

10. The Government does not believe that it would be right for health authorities or boards also to be able to act as providers of general medical or dental services, for example, by directly employing doctors or dentists. The division between purchasing and providing should be retained here, consistent with health authorities' and boards' other responsibilities in relation to hospital and community health services. The provision for health authorities or boards if necessary to employ doctors or dentists under Section 56 of the 1977 NHS Act (and Section 33 of the 1978 NHS (Scotland) Act) would remain. Section 56 is a reserve power to deal with the unusual situation where the provision of services to a locality or part of a locality is inadequate. It enables the Secretary of State to step in and either authorise, or himself make, other and different arrangements to cover "exceptional circumstances".

11. <u>Pilots and the Medical and Dental Lists</u>. There will clearly need to be security for doctors or dentists who enter into pilots to return to the existing arrangements if a pilot ends.

Doctors

Should the pilot end for any reason a doctor would need to be able to return to the Medical List for his or her authority or board and to the current contract without having to re-apply to the Medical Practices Committee (Scottish Medical Practices Committee in Scotland) provided the remaining existing criteria relating to the Medical List were met, for example, those on age. The only exception to this would be where the pilot terminated or a doctor left the scheme in circumstances where there were serious allegations about his or her fitness to practice. In those circumstances the Government considers that the NHS Tribunal should consider whether return to the list was appropriate. In all other respects the pilots would be separate from the existing arrangements, including the current rules on vacancies and admission to the Medical List although the Medical Practices Committee and the Scottish Medical Practices Committee would be expected to take account of any pilot practices in determining the distribution of practitioners under Part II of the 1977 or 1978 Acts. It would however be important to ensure there remained a coherent local and national view of the overall GP workforce and its distribution.

Dentists

Dentists are not subject to the same restrictions as doctors. They have a right to be included in a health authority or health board List if they are vocationally trained (or are exempt or have equivalent qualifications). This right will be retained. They will also be able to remain on a health authority or health board List while working under a contract for the new system. However, where a dentist chooses to work solely in a pilot and has his or her contract terminated following serious allegations relating to professional misconduct, the Government considers that before being allowed on a health authority or health board List, the NHS Tribunal should be able to consider whether inclusion of his or her name on the list would be appropriate. Dentists will not be required to be included on a health authority or health board List to be considered for a contract. Health authorities and health boards will note on their proposals to the Secretary of State the qualifications, experience and participation in relevant postgraduate activities of each of the dentists who would be working under the proposal and this will be taken into account by the Secretary of State when deciding whether the pilot should be approved.

12. <u>Complaints and Breaches of Contract</u>. As with the existing contractual arrangements, pilots would need to make provision for complaints and breaches of contract ("discipline"). There should be provision for the Secretary of State to determine what should be included, including any arbitration and appeal rights should disputes arise and where termination of the contract is proposed. The Health Service Commissioner should continue to be responsible for investigating complaints by, or on behalf of, individuals who claim to have

- make arrangements for evaluation of a pilot, including approving the criteria and process;

- require health authorities and boards to monitor the quality of the service provided;

- require health authorities and boards to provide information locally about the pilot to those affected, particularly on the quality, volume and cost of services so as to ensure patients are protected and tax payers receive value for money and on the criteria for evaluation and the process for doing so.

In addition of course the centre would issue guidance on the nature of pilots and their development as it does now for example with general medical services and fundholding.

CHOICE AND OPPORTUNITY

Primary Care:
The Future

Presented to Parliament by the Secretary of State
for Health by Command of Her Majesty
October 1996

First Published 1996
Reprinted 1997

Cm 3390   £5.30

THE UNIVERSITY

19 MAY

BIBLIOGRAPHY

Service Developments

"Primary Care: The Future". 1996. Department of Health.

"Primary Care: The Way Forward in Wales". 1996. Welsh Office.

"Primary Care: The Way Ahead". 1996. Scottish Home and Health Department.

"Maintaining Medical Excellence". Chief Medical Officer's Review of Guidance on Doctors' Performance 1995.

"Fundamental Review of Dental Remuneration: Report of Sir Kenneth Bloomfield KCB. 1992.

"4th Report: Dental Services. Health Select Committee". 1993. HMSO. 264 - 1.

"Improving NHS Dentistry". 1994. HMSO. Cm 2625.

Printed in the UK for The Stationery Office Limited on behalf
of the Controller of Her Majesty's Stationery Office
Dd 5067749   10/97   2200   77569   Job No. J0029520